BLITZER, A DOBERMAN THE NECK AND LIMBS, CONT "I BELIEVE IN IT (MASSAGE THERAPY). I KNOW FIRST HAND THAT IT WORKS. *BLITZ* IS LIVING PROOF. IF MASSAGE HADN'T WORKED, HE WOULD HAVE BEEN PUT TO SLEEP. HE WENT FROM COMPLETE PARALYSIS BACK TO BEING A NORMAL DOG."—B. PEOPLES, TOLEDO, OH.

KORY, IS A BOUVIER DES FLANDRES WITH SEVERE ARTHRITIS: "I USED TO SPEND ABOUT $100 A MONTH IN SHOTS FOR KORY, BUT I WASN'T SEEING MUCH PROGRESS. AFTER ONE MASSAGE I COULD SEE THAT IT HELPED OUT. KORY ISN'T CURED OF ARTHRITIS, BUT HE SURE CAN WALK BETTER."— R.McNIVEN, SOUTHGATE, MI.

A POODLE WHO CANNOT JUMP ONTO A COUCH,
A BEAGLE WITH NUMB FORELIMBS STRUGGLES TO WALK,
A POMERANIAN WITH CURVED SPINE, WALKS SIDEWAYS,
A ROTTWEILER CRIPPLED WITH HIP PAIN, IS IRRITABLE,
A GOLDEN RETRIEVER GRIEVES HER KENNEL-MATE,
AN OLD ENGLISH SHEEPDOG WITH ALLERGIES, MANGE AND DYSPLASIA, IS UNCOMFORTABLE & VERY SAD,
YOUNG, OLD, HEALTHY, SICK, COMPANION, SHOW, OBEDIENCE, ASSISTANCE, AND *YOUR* DOGS

ALL BENEFIT FROM...

EFFECTIVE PET MASSAGE FOR DOGS

Other works by Jonathan Rudinger:

Effective Pet Massage for Dogs,
Complete Basic Dog Massage Demonstration,
Volume 1(videocassette)

Effective Pet Massage for Older Dogs,
Advanced lessons for Geriatric, Upper Spine, Respiratory
Enhancement, Hips, Volume 2 (videocassette)

EFFECTIVE PET MASSAGE FOR DOGS

With Jonathan Rudinger, LMT, RN

- Learn to massage your dog for a healthy, happy lifetime

- Simple, easy-to-follow instructions

- Complete massage demonstration

- Special geriatric section

- Advanced lessons on hips, upper spine and respiratory techniques

Dedicated to Anastasia & Samantha.

In Memory of Ruth, Irv, & Pepper.

Massage is not, nor is it intended to be a substitute for traditional veterinary care. It is a complementary form of health care. The information is provided for the purposes of education and to give as complete a description as possible. The reader should regularly consult a veterinarian in matters relating to his or her dog's health and especially in regard to any symptoms, which may require diagnosis or medical attention. If you have any questions regarding the efficacy of any of the techniques suggested in this manual, please consult with your veterinarian or qualified animal massage therapist.

Working with any animal involves inherent risk. While general massage techniques are all to be applied lovingly and gently, any receiver, animal or human, will react negatively to strokes that may feel abusive, invasive, or inappropriate. The authors and agents of Effective Pet Massage for Dogs, assume no risk for injury incurred while learning to massage your dog.

Cover design by Chrystal Bostian/Multimedia Counselors, Inc. Cover Photography by Cheryl Hall.

Includes index
ISBN 0-9664826-2-X

Forward and acknowledgements

In the summer of 1998, I was interviewed by a Toledo, OH television station as part of a series called "Pampered Pets." I was demonstrating equine massage, describing the benefits that horses receive from massotherapy. My host, Melissa Voetsch, at the end of the segment brought over an old Golden Retriever, and said, "Dogs get stiff backs too. Let's see what Jonathan can do." And as I leaned over to cradle the dog's head in my hands, I experienced one of those "Aha's," that only rarely do I get an opportunity to feel.

I *knew* at that moment that everything I had done and learned up to that point in my life had prepared me for working with dogs. Well, we started getting phone calls and invitations to give presentations, TV, radio and newspaper interviews. I started seeing canine clients in their homes and at veterinary clinics. I've had such wonderful support wherever I've discussed pet massage, that Anastasia Drabik-Rudinger, my life partner and editor, and I produced first one video and then another, as a home study course to teach people to massage their dogs. This manual is the accompanying text.

I would like to thank Melissa for her encouragement. Thanks to Paul Kwapich, for his videography and editing skills for *EPM, Vol. 1*. Mike Malone, videographer, Harry Frank, Editor, Roger Grieve, Producer & Zeta Productions for their invaluable expertise for *EPM, Vol.2*, and Cheryl Hall, who shares the copyright on many of the photos in this manual.

My thanks to my canine talent, Shooter, Gracie, Oreo and Peter, and to their human companions who graciously gave permission for them to be in the videos and this manual, Aslynn Roe, who set the design of this text. Special gratitude goes to Jane Lindsey for expertise and patience in formatting this text as I made changes. To Anastasia, whose patience and understanding withstood my working on this magnificent obsession: thank you. ¬JR

Contents

What humans can learn from dogs...

Never pass up the opportunity to go for a joy ride.
Allow the experience of fresh air and wind in your face to be pure ecstasy.
When loved ones come home, always run to greet them.
When it's in your best interest, practice obedience.

Dogs know that doing these things makes you happy...

Let others know when they have invaded your territory.
Take naps and stretch before rising.
Run, romp and play daily.
Eat with gusto and enthusiasm.
Be loyal.

More advise from canines on happier living...

Never pretend to be something you're not.
If what you want lies buried, dig until you find it.
When someone is having a bad day, be silent, sit close by and nuzzle him or her gently.
Thrive on attention and let people touch you.

No matter how often you are scolded, don't buy into the guilt thing and pout; run right back and make friends.

Simple tricks for easier living from a dog's point of view...

Avoid biting when a simple growl will do.

On hot days drink lots of water or be under a shady tree.

When you're happy, dance around and wag your entire body.

Delight in the simple joy of a long walk.

No matter how often you are scolded, don't buy into the guilt thing and pout; run right back and make friends.

To many of us, dogs are soul mates,
trusted companions for many years.

Part 1 The Importance of Massage

Why I wrote this manual for you

Dogs are more than our best friends. They are companions, protectors and comforters. Our dogs do more than greet us when we come home; they trust us and love us unconditionally. To many of us, dogs are soul mates, trusted companions for many years. *Effective Pet Massage for Dogs* is designed to teach humans the skills to enhance the bond between human and canine, to give back to their animals, and to empower them to responsibly and effectively care for their dogs.

Massage reduces stress, aids in healing and provides ongoing health care for your pet. By giving your dog the gift of massage, you are rewarding him/her for a lifetime of companionship and friendship.

> *Massage is more than petting or play. It is a deliberate and focused technique of touching.*

People often ask whether day to day petting counts as massage. I respond, "No." Let me explain why. Massage is more than petting or play, it is a deliberate and focused technique of touching your dog. Each stroke is controlled in pressure, direction and intention. Your hands become finely tuned tools of assessment, finely tuned sensing devices. They are also the conduits through which healing and love flow.

> ***Your hands are finely tuned tools of assessment, finely tuned sensing devices. They are also the conduits through which healing and love flow.***

As a Registered Nurse and Licensed Massage Therapist, I have been trained extensively in human anatomy and physiology. As a horseback riding enthusiast for most of my life, I have also developed an intuitive understanding and healthy respect for the power and danger of working with and around animals.

I found that many of the same skills I utilized in massaging humans worked for my horses and dogs. I have studied T'ai Ch'i Chuan, and sensory disciplines, as well. I've learned that by engaging animals in deliberate massage has allowed me to communicate on many levels. In the course of learning the craft of massaging dogs, my sensory perception has increased dramatically; this helps me feel more at one with all my clients.

When we tune into the needs and fears of our dogs we learn to understand the subtle cues-the body language they use to communicate with each other and with us, *if* we are open and receptive.

With humans in normal conversation as much as 85% of communication is non-verbal. How we stand, how we distribute our weight, is our face uplifted or looking at the ground, are our fists clenched or hands open, are knees locked or softly flexed, are arms or legs crossed, are we breathing easily or holding our breath? These are all subtle ways that we and our pets speak with our bodies and our minds.

> *I would like you to understand this beautiful language and incorporate your response in the language of conscious touch.*

Massage

First of all, let's talk about what massage is. Massage is the manipulation of muscles and skin to promote increased circulation to all the organs and tissues in your pet's body.

Why would we want to do this?

Increases blood circulation

Each cell and muscle fiber in the body must be constantly bathed in fresh, oxygen-laden blood. This blood, along with oxygen brings the required hormones, nutrients, and proteins, necessary for normal cell growth. As it circulates, it removes the waste products of cell metabolism and transports these wastes to organs in the body, which will filter them out. Blood normally flows *around* inactive muscles and *through* active ones. The varying pressures applied during massage help move the blood, increasing circulation to all the tissues and cells in the body.

> *The sense of touch brings a oneness, comfort and tranquility. Psychologists have proven that touch is a need, just as important as food or water.*

Increases lymph movement

The lymph is a clear fluid that contains white blood cells. White Blood cells are the work force of the immune system. Whenever there is a need for them to be anywhere in the body they must get there through the lymphatic system, which runs similar to the venous blood system. Massage not only moves the blood through the muscles and the lymph through the lymphatic system, but it also enhances the flow of Ch'i (energy) throughout the life force meridians (channels) of the body.

You are the first line of defense for your dog; the best source in the treatment of your pet's health conditions and well being.

The body is a conduit of bio-electrical and magnetic energy fields. This is acknowledged and has been used in every known human culture since the dawn of time.

The phenomena of electrical impulses and magnetic lines of circuitry are the basis of acupressure points and meridian pathways. Meridian pathways are a series of points on the *surface* of the skin that, when touched, influences the balance of energy flow in the body. By touching, holding and stimulating specific spots on the surface of the body, we can utilize these pathways of energy channels to rebalance systems of organs deep inside. This is part of the discipline of Traditional Chinese Medicine. Acupressure points are spots that are pressed to release endorphins; the body's own painkillers.

Massage is nonverbal communication. Even before language, the power of touch made contacts between individuals both physical and spiritual. Just as volumes can be written in a single glance, so too can deep levels of conscious and unconscious  conversations transpire with the simple touch. It is a way of expressing ourselves, both profound and elemental.

On the conscious level we can assess temperature, pulse rate and its quality. We can measure the depth of respiration, dryness in coat and skin texture and integrity. We can feel tightness in muscles and tendons, and the qualities of some bone interactions at joints. These will give you physical assessments.

On an unconscious level, we sense disease, fear or emotional instability. They are in the subtle body movements which our hearts can read that elude our minds. Tapping into this conversation helps us become better facilitators for our pets' healing.

Your dog craves this touch, this reassuring warmth from you. Notice when you're lying on your side how he seems to always rest his head on the space behind your bent knee. The area behind your knee is one of the places on your body where the blood is closest to the surface. You can actually take your pulse in this spot. This is one example of how your dog keeps a constant assessment of your well being, too.

> *Notice when you're lying on your side how he seems to always rest his head on the space behind your bent knee.*

Power of touch

Touch brings a oneness, comfort and tranquility. It is often necessary, especially in very young puppies to externally stimulate them to activate internal systems: e.g. opening their eyes and the defecation response. Failure to thrive in infants and in animals is directly related to the quality and quantity of touch received. Psychologists have proven that touch is a basic, essential need, just as food or water.

The first thing a new mother does after giving birth is hold and caress her baby. It expresses her love and caring. It verifies reality and it confirms the presence of the precious new life. Mother and father both learn to bond with the baby through respectful and compassionate touching.

Animals bond in very complex ways using many more senses than touch such as scent, hearing and several nondefinable internal senses. Roger Caras, in *A Dog Is Listening,* describes how these are not only beyond our own capabilities, but beyond our comprehension. But, with massage, you can give your dog an essential component of nurturing and care.

In my human massage practice, I have seen seniors who have lost their partners break down in tears during a massage. Why? Because it had been so long since anyone had touched them. This is the power of touch. This is the power of massage.

Failure to thrive in infants and in animals is directly related to the quality and quantity of touch received.

Canine Benefits

Why do dogs need or benefit from massage? Massage is physical therapy, as well as mind/spiritual therapy. It helps to rebalance the body to live and move in harmony and grace. Massage relieves pain and discomfort naturally by releasing the naturally produced chemicals (endorphins) in our dog's and our bodies.

Our bodies are ingenious and incredible chemical factories and distribution networks. When it needs to heal itself, the body knows to produce and deliver precisely the correct combinations of chemicals in the exact doses at the right time and by exactly the correct pathway.

So, without the use of external drugs, very often your pet's body can assume control of his own pain relieving mechanism. Sometimes, though, he/she may need a little helpful encouragement: *your* controlled, skillful touch.

Massage is a complement to, not a substitute for, your pet's own health maintaining abilities, and, of course, your veterinarian's compassionate and qualified care.

> ***Sometimes, though, he/she may need a little helpful encouragement.***

Dr Michael Fox says in, *The Healing Touch,* that pet massage has "both physical and psychological benefits. It is almost essential care, like grooming, feeding and exercise." He goes on to say "pets who are confined indoors will benefit from massage. Older animals who suffer from chronic and degenerative disorders such as muscular cramps, stiffness, arthritis and some skin conditions will also benefit."

Increasing circulation throughout your entire pet's body helps and maintains the healing process. The dog also experiences the sense of empowerment from the person who is giving the massage. Dr. Ruth James notes in *The*

Dog Repair Book, that massage is often used in addition to heat treatments to heal minor sprains. It helps keep scar tissue from forming adhesions and reduces swelling and pain. She recommends a massage "should be given three or four times a day with only the bare hands."

> ***Older animals who suffer from chronic and degenerative disorders benefit with massage.***

Healthy dogs

The acronym **H-E-A-L-T-H-Y** brings together many aspects of care.

H-Healthful diet
E-Early detection and intervention
A-Activity
L-Longtime Pal
T-TLC
H-History
Y-You

H- Healthful diet: Check with your veterinarian, or trainer to make sure your dog has a diet balanced with his activity level. All aspects of your dog need adequate nutrition. Every cell in your dog's body needs an oxygen rich diet. Massage provides physical, energetic and emotional nourishment, giving support and touch-reassurance.

E- Early detection & intervention: Massage is hands-on observation. Also, be aware of any changes you feel on the skin or notice in your dog's gait, disposition, eating and bowel habits. If you sense anything unusual contact your vet to get advice. Stress reduction is an intervention. Reduce stress with massage.

Older dogs chill easier and are more susceptible to dehydration and heat exhaustion. In this they are similar to older humans. Appropriate housing and protection are necessities. Since senses are not as sharp as they were, decrease your dog's time in front of the air conditioner or heating duct. Muscles can tighten up or skin may burn.

A- Activity burns calories and maintains joint flexibility. Lack of movement is the cause of much deterioration in muscle, bone and nerves. If your dog has reduced his level of activity, you can help him make up the difference to maintain a healthy body with massage.

L- Longtime Pal: You can depend on your dog being there for you his entire lifetime. And he can depend on you.

T- TLC: Tender Lovin' Care, you're giving it through massage.

> *In some cases, massage can even be an alternative to surgery.*

H- History/genetics: Your dog's history can give you a good idea of what his present health is and what his future will be.

Physically, he/she has already established weakened or vulnerable areas. The sites of old surgeries, sprains, and broken bones, although healed, are the places where muscular or bone degeneration will occur first.

Emotionally, his/her memories of past events and the attachment and associations with these memories have defined a sensitive, neurotic, and unique personality. Acknowledging limitations and fears will help you give the support that's needed.

Genetically, the script is written. However, massage can decrease physical discomfort and emotional distress. It will help maintain muscle tone and good bone density despite the genetic predisposition.

Y- You: At this crucial time in your dog's life, only you can make his/her life more comfortable. Make the decision to help any way possible.

Your dog is your soul mate

There are many wonderful books written on the subject of dogs. Written by veterinarians, breeders, groomers, trainers or animal rescue agents, they cover most of what one needs to know about our canine friends. They cover selecting, breeding, training, nutrition and medical care, pet control, and socially responsible dilemmas on neutering and euthanasia.

> *In older pets, it is an excellent tonic for joint afflictions and decreased range of motion.*

What is offered here in this array of information is a unique perspective on empowering the relationship between pet and owner through hands-on massage.

As a complement to traditional medical care massage can be used to increase blood flow and influence healing time, decreasing it in post-operative situations. In some cases, massage can even be an alternative to surgery.

In older pets, massage is an excellent tonic for joint afflictions and decreased range of motion. When animals are in pain or agitated, the soothing effects of massage can give them the calmness necessary for healing to take place.

I am glad you have taken the initiative to learn dog massage. It is an easy to learn program and one you will enjoy almost as much as your dog will. Massage will enhance your bond with your dog so that he/she can live a fuller, longer and happy life.

Pay attention to your dog. What is he telling you?

Is your dog limping or favoring one leg over another? Is he listless or not eating regularly? Does his spine arch to one side? When walking or trotting, does he track in a straight path? Have his eating habits or bowel movements changed? Does he chill easily? Is he moving slower? Does your friend lay in one position most of the time?

> *Does your friend lay in one position most of the time?*

Be alert to behaviors your dog expresses. This is part of his/her body language. More cues to look for are unusual textures or patterns in his coat. Are there sore or tender areas that are just not healing? Are his eyes bright or dull? These too, are all indicators of your dog's well being.

Sometimes, direct massage is not the answer.

There are several times when massage is not recommended. However, each of these times would be a perfect opportunity to do off-the-body therapies by massaging the areas, while not directly touching it. You will need to keep an inch or two above the skin. These are contraindications.

Do not administer direct massage:

- if your dog has lesions or has been diagnosed with cancer.

- over open wounds, blisters or abrasions.

- on recent fractures, although gentle massage directly above and below *in the direction toward the heart* will increase blood flow and decrease healing time.

- if your dog has a fever.

> ***Do <u>not</u> administer firm direct massage if your dog has been diagnosed with cancer.***

Guidelines for massage

🦴 Set up a regular time to massage your dog. He/she is worth twenty minutes of your day or week for quality, undivided time. Your first few sessions may probably last only 10 minutes. As you build confidence and assuredness in your techniques, both you and your dog will learn to enjoy and look forward to each massage session.

🦴 Provide some soft, non-threatening music. It will help both of you to relax and unwind.

🦴 Wash your hands before you start. Dogs have very sensitive noses and the smell of food on your hands will distract them.

Do not massage immediately after feeding. Massage directly affects the digestive process.

Do not massage while food is cooking; the aromas, again, will surely be distracting to both of you.

Do not massage when you are focusing on other plans or activities. Give your friend your undivided attention.

> ***Wash your hands.***
> ***Dogs have very sensitive noses.***
> ***The smell of food on your hands***
> ***is distracting.***

Remember your breathing needs to be in harmony with the massage techniques you are applying. Again, you will find it relaxes you, too.

Before each massage session, ask for permission and wait to receive your answer. Dogs have moods, just like people. There will be times when he/she is more receptive to touch than others.

Maintaining contact with both hands is essential. As you stroke your dog's body with one hand, be sure to maintain contact with the other hand. It holds the body in position so you can comfortably reach where you need to touch. It supports and reassures him/her that you are there for him as a healing and loving presence. On an energetic level you are maintaining a closed and continuous bio-electrical-magnetic circuit by keeping both hands on your dog.

Do not massage when you are focusing on other plans or activities.

Give your friend your undivided attention.

Location and positioning

Choose a place without distraction. Turn off the phone, TV, computer and kids for just a little while. Keep other pets from wandering into the area. This is his/her special time and place with you. You'll both enjoy this break of quiet time.

Locations will vary depending on the size, disposition and personality of your dog. You can sit on the floor or on a campstool if your larger dog is on the ground. You may want to massage your medium sized friend on a grooming table, picnic table, coffee table, or if he is little, on your lap.

It is important too, that your dog has secure footing and that the work surface is stable and solid.

You can administer massage with the dog standing, sitting, or lying on his side or on his stomach. If he is on his back it is difficult to reach many of the massage areas, and massage is more than just a tummy rub. Just make sure you can comfortably reach your hands all over his entire body.

There will be times when you will need to hold the dog against your body for support and times when you'll have to position him/her so you can work specific areas of the body. The location you choose needs to be comfortable for *you;* only then will it be a relaxing time for both of you.

> **Massage is more than just a tummy rub.**

Verbal support

Very often, the pace and gentleness of your voice has a lot to do with the overall mood and acceptance of the therapy session. It is certainly okay to talk to your dog, reassuring him/her that the massage is going well and thanking him for the opportunity to assist in the healing process. Dogs comprehend our language, too  (sometimes more than we would like); and while they may not understand all the specific meanings of our words, they readily understand the tone, the intent and the body language used at the time the words are said. That is the reason you always ask for permission out loud before you start to give massage therapy. Wait for the okay, then proceed.

Dogs have moods, as we all know. They get headaches, they get sad, and they grieve the loss of people, objects, and familiar surroundings. Massage is a very effective way to comfort those who are hurting, but there may be some times when they just don't want to be touched. Their needs must be honored. Time spent in their "cave" may be more therapeutic than touch for the moment. But, that's rare. Dogs love to be touched, they *need* to be stroked, and most are eager to receive their massages whenever and as often as they can get them.

Balanced Strokes

Each stroke in a massage must be balanced. Each section of the massage must be balanced. The reason you are giving the massage is to balance your dog.

Each stroke or touch is unique and singular. It starts, has a middle and has an end. For example, slowly rest your hands on your dog's shoulder. Be aware of the softness as your hands land on the area. Allow them to linger without increasing or decreasing pressure, then softly allow your hands to lift from the surface.

When pressing in, push and exit with similar rates of speed and pressure. This will give balance to each stroke. Concentrate on how your hands are moving. After a little practice this will become a natural part of your massage technique. But every so often, remember to check that each touch is balanced.

This is massage in a nutshell: Treat each body section as an entity that also has a beginning, middle and end. Start slowly, getting permission from your dog to work each area. Warm the muscles, identify areas which may need more attention, work the areas, use *smoothing* strokes to integrate the healing process into the rest of the body systems, and gently lift your hands away from the surface.

Balance both sides. Whatever therapy you do to one side must be done on the other. Muscles may not appear to have the same tightness or soreness; but, the ones on the "healthy" side need to be supported as well. They've been working extra hard while the "hurt" side has been resting, contracted in a guarded posture, or unable to pull its weight.

> *One of the ways your dog integrates the stimulation or balancing of his body systems is to give himself a good shake.*

Massage *is* balance. Begin slowly with slow, flowing assessment strokes, reading and listening to your dog. Choose the types of strokes, pressures, rates of movement would best suit your dog at this moment (each massage is different in content, mood and in character). Move from area to area, developing and completing each before moving to the next.

Complete as you began, with slow, flowing *smoothing* strokes. This is the way of balance.

Applying pressure

Usually, we can gauge the amount of pressure to use by projecting the feel of our touch back onto ourselves. Ask, what would this feel like if I were doing this to myself? You already know, instinctively, the pressure to be used to seaywithin the comfort range of your dog. A large, heavily muscled and thick-coated animal will naturally be able to tolerate more pressure than, say, a whippet or toy poodle. A hearty vigorous massage can act as a tonic for older, weaker dogs. More gentle techniques are used for dogs that need to be gentled, are in a traumatic process, or who are in recovery.

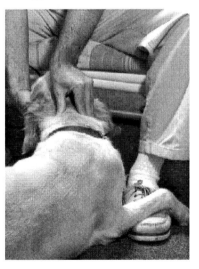

A hard, deep massage is not always the most effective. Jabbing directly into the muscles can be abusive and may actually damage muscle tissue. The pressure you apply needs to be just enough to feel contours of the underlying structures beneath the coat, skin and fatty areas. Excessive use of pressure reduces the sensitivity in our fingertips and palms. Too much pressure and too much speed may put your dog into a "play mode" reducing the therapeutic benefits of massage.

Always be careful when applying pressure with your thumbs. Human thumbs are very strong and can exert more force than you realize. The amount of pressure you should apply is normally about two or three pounds. To understand how much this is (or rather isn't), close your eyes (after you have read this paragraph). Use your fingers to make small circles on your eyelid without pressing on the eye itself. That is all the pressure you usually need when massaging your dog.

Often, in massage, we only need to bring your dog's focus to a specific spot. And *this is very light touch.* As an exercise, place a nickel on the back of your hand. Now practice touching your hand with only that slight amount of pressure. That's all you'll need.

Don't worry that he'll be able to feel it. Your dog is aware of the weight of a fly when it lands on his body; any touch is ponderous by comparison.

When applying compression to large muscle groups such as those on the upper foreleg, visualize that you are gently squeezing the water out of a large natural sponge. More specific techniques, instructions and suggestions are in each of the sections throughout this manual.

> *Set up a regular time to massage your dog. Your pet is worth twenty minutes out of your day or week for quality, undivided time.*

Rate

The speed of your movements will determine the mood of the session. If your movements are quick, the effects will be stimulating. If the strokes used are long and slow, the effects will be more relaxing. As you become more confident in giving massage, you'll be able to sense that some areas on the body seem more sluggish than others and will need some increased circulation. Some may be hyper and may need to be quieted. In each massage session, use your intuition about the needs and requests of your dog. You'll be using a variety of strokes in a wide range of tempos.

It is very important to maintain an even rate of breathing. Modulate your strokes, initially 1 stroke to 1 breath, until you get used to working while bending over, reaching around or across your dog. Remember: **_DO NOT GET OUT OF BREATH_**.

As soon as you start huffing and puffing, both you and your dog will lose most of the benefits of the massage. You surely won't be enjoying the process, so you probably won't want to continue. Then both you and your dog will miss out on some terrific therapy.

How to get your dog to sit still

🦴 Allow yourself uninterrupted time and don't worry about a set time frame for the massage.

🦴 Make sure he has relieved himself before you begin.

🦴 Reduce distractions before you begin. Don't give him a bone or toy before the massage, as it will only distract him.

🦴 Notice if your dog gets overstimulated and if he does, stop.

🦴 Allow him to move away. When he's ready, he will come back. If not, he's had enough massage for this session.

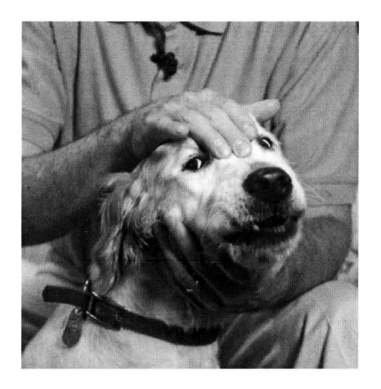

 Give your pet time to learn to utilize the healing power of massage. He will learn to stay longer as his attention span increases. Sessions can last up to 45 minutes.

Part 2 Massage Techniques

Hand positions

Open hand:

applies gentle pressure with hands and fingers extended over any flat surface. Used for long, flowing strokes from head to rump. Also used in *tapping*.

Curved hand:

allows your hand to follow the contours of the head, limbs and chest. The hand is held supple so that the relaxed palm and fingers can move evenly over curved contours. It is used in long flowing strokes and in compression. *Curved hand* is also used to warm and quiet an area needing attention.

Thumb walk:

used for direct application of gentle pressure on specific points. It is used primarily around the eyes, skull, ears, and on either side of the spine. Hold your hands as shown in the illustration. As you maintain contact/support with your fingers, your thumbs are freed and flexible to move from position to position. The movement is to gently touch, press in slowly, hold, slowly release, and then pause, before moving on to the next spot.

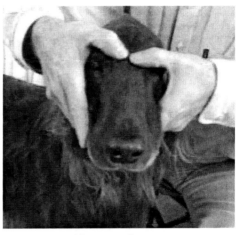

Use the *pads* of the thumbs, not the tips. You won't have as much sensitivity on the tip of the thumb. If you use the tips, including the edge of the thumbnail, you'll have lost the subtlety of control and may be applying too much pressure. Adjust the amount of pressure by levering your hand up or down while maintaining softened (relaxed) thumb-knuckle joints. *Thumb walking* is sensitive and subtle work. Your thumbs will soon learn to react to tiny variances in bio-electric charges and muscle tension.

Clasp hands:

Join fingers of both hands together underneath the animal and gently pull upward, hold, and slowly lower.

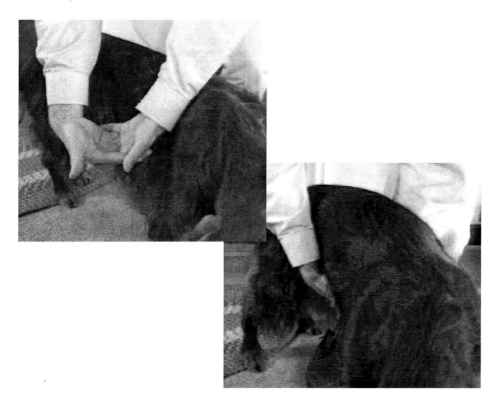

Massage Strokes
you will need to know:

Effleurage:
simple touch combined with movement, light friction. This is most similar to the long even petting strokes you already do. These strokes are long, slow, even-pressured and flowing hand movements. Pressure is light to medium.

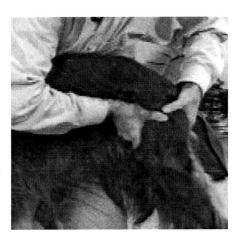

Compression:
or pressing onto the surface of the body with thumbs, fingers, palms, using one or both hands, as in gently squeezing water out of a wet sponge.

Joint movement:

The type of movement we will be using is passive movement of the joints or limbs. This means *you*

will be doing all the work of lifting and moving the limb back and forth at the moveable points, the joints. Older, stiffer dogs or those with arthritis will initially resist this movement, but stay with it. As you continue, they will relax and regain some of their flexibility.

Support (hold) that part closest to the main body of your dog with one hand, and with your working hand, grasp just below the next joint

down. Slowly and gently move the leg, or tail in small circles or if it's a joint that only moves back and forth like the elbow or paw, back and forth.

Do not stretch the joint, or attempt to force it into a movement that it resists. Your dog will know his/her own limits and range of comfortable motion.

After a couple of sessions, close your eyes and feel the borders of the range of motion where you feel the beginnings of resistance. You will notice your dog's *increased flexibility* as well as his *decreased stiffness and discomfort* with regular massage!

**Do not stretch the joints,
or attempt to force them
into movements that they resist.**

**Your dog will know his own
limits and range of his
comfortable motion.**

Tapping:

is gentle percussion used primarily on the top of the head and over tightened muscle areas, such as the shoulders or hamstrings. This is used very rarely but is very much appreciated when done correctly. There are 2 types of tapping. One is using the Open hand position and the other is with Curved hand.

Hold your Open hand flat, with fingers extended (see Open hand). Movement onto the head is made from the wrist as your fingertips softly bop down on the top of your dog's head. Tap across the top, above the eyes, to the edges of the ears and across the back of the skull. The rate is about 4 per second, slower, if that's more comfortable for you. This movement rebalances the cerebral spinal fluid that encases and cushions the brain within the skull. Try this with your fingertips to yourself. It is a terrific brain stimulator/rebalancer!

Applied to the shoulders or hamstrings, hold your hands in a loose Curved Hand position. With fingers relaxed and held slightly apart, hold them sideways—thumbs on top. All movement stems from your flexed wrist, gently hack the area with the sides of your palm.

It isn't recommended to tap for more than 3 or 4 seconds on any one site during a session.

Skin rolling:

is the lifting of the coat and skin away from the underlying structures, such as the muscles, bones and fat.   This stretches the connective tissue under the skin increasing pliability, and general skin tone. Grasp the coat and roll it between your thumb and fingers. Take care to avoid pinching. This should be a rhythmic, rolling motion. As one handful of coat is released back to the body, another is picked up.

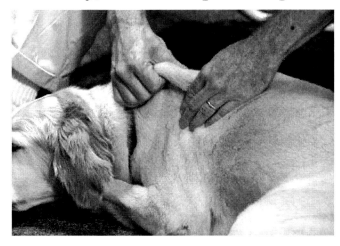

Vibration:

the rapid back and forth movement of your hand or fingers as they touch your dog's body.

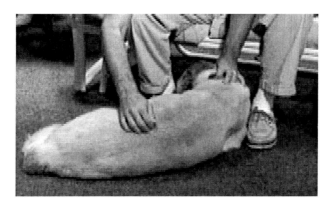

Smoothing:

integrates the previous sequences and energetically balances your dog in preparation for the next step. It is done quickly with Curved hand and smoothes the coat while making your dog feel secure.

 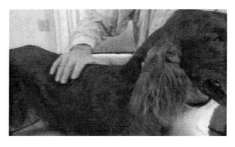

Suggested rates

These are suggested rates of movement. Please experiment to discover the timing that is most comfortable for you, the Massage Therapist.

Vibratory movements are as fast as your hand can agitate,

Light tapping at about 4 per second,

Skin rolling the coat at about 1-2 per second,

Light stroking/smoothing at approximately the length of your dogs limb or tail per second (yes, even cropped tails),

Assessment strokes at the rate of 2-4 inches per second.

Allow your hands to pause and rest quietly over any area which requests attention. Listen to your dog's body's language.

> *When you hold your breath, your hands tighten up. They lose their gentleness, flexibility and sensitivity. Your dog will feel the difference.*

Take your time and don't forget to breathe. When you start to hold your breath, your hands tighten up losing their gentleness, flexibility and sensitivity. Your dog will be able to feel the difference. If you need to regulate the rhythm of your breathing, try 1 breath for each stroke, or every 2 strokes. You'll find the rhythm that works for you.

Part 3
Introduction and Assessment Sequence.

Once you have become comfortable with the following Introduction and Assessment sequence, an essential part of every massage, this part should only take 5-10 minutes to complete per session.

The rule of threes

In the first part of the massage we will be working in three stroke groups. You will be talked through the first set of stroking passes; we'll describe what you may be feeling and what these sensations mean. Then your hands will be directed over particular routes to systematically touch-cover and assess your dog's entire body.

> *This part should only take 5-10 minutes to complete per session.*

The top line

Start with 2 passes. Start at the tip of the nose, moving over the top of the head, over the spine and to the tip of the tail. With Open Hands, make the first pass. These are the most like petting, only with more deliberateness and focused caring. They are saying, "Thank you for permission to give you a massage. Okay, we're starting now. We are now going to spend some really special time together. The pace of my strokes is establishing a mood. The love in each touch will help you to feel stronger and more balanced."

Introduction strokes:
2 Effleurage,
light stroking
passes--slowly,
gently & evenly.

The third pass is
a firm, deliberate
Assessment
stroke.

The third pass is different. It is slower still, firmer and even more deliberate. This is an *Assessment* stroke. Use your hands and fingers as sensing devises as they move over the head, neck and bumps of the spine and tail.

Assess for what? During the third pass, feel for tightness in the muscles, warm or cool areas or changes in texture of the coat. Feel for lumps, warts and pockets of fat under the skin. Note any tender spots or unusual hair growth patterns.

Muscle tightness or "knots" in the muscle tissue could be caused by the bunching up of fascia, or the connective tissue in and around muscles and under the skin. Overwork, injuries, strain or muscle spasms could all be reasons that this fascia has gotten stuck and lost its elasticity. They could stem from incorrect skeletal alignment or any discomfort, which would lead to your dog guarding against pain by restricting his/her own movements.

Warm areas could be signs of bruises or areas of infection where your dog's blood has pooled beneath the surface of the skin. Warm areas can be found at an injury site as a natural healing process. Our bodies and our dogs' bodies have the marvelous ability to heal themselves. Your sensing this heat is an opportunity for you to become aware of this miracle while it is happening.

> *Sensing this heat is an opportunity for you to become aware of the miracle while it is happening.*

Cool areas are often the sites of old injuries, or surgeries, where there may be incomplete/reduced blood circulation to the site, or stagnation of energy flow.

Lumps and warts are common in older dogs. If you notice any changes in them from one massage to the next, then refer to your veterinarian for advice.

> *Feel for tightness in the muscles, cool areas, bumps, warts and pockets of fat under the skin.*

You may be detecting serious disease symptoms early on, in time to get effective, yet minimal, medical treatment. This early detection is one of the best reasons to consistently include this part of the massage sequence in each session.

 Fatty pockets under the skin may be just fat, but then again, they could be indicators of health problems. Bring these to your vet's attention and then keep a vigilant eye on these areas and watch for any changes. The changes we're referring to are not really measurable except that you will note "a change." That's all you need to do. Assess it, note it, keep an eye on it, and if it changes, tell your vet.

> ***Uneven hair patterns or colic may indicate an underlying organ or tissue is unhealthy.***

Tender spots will be readily apparent. Your dog will definitely let you know when you touch one by moving away from you, yelping or collapsing away from the pressure. These may be bruises, sprains or otherwise injured tissue. They may also be sites of chronic discomfort such as arthritis or hip dysplasia.

Uneven hair patterns or colic may indicate an underlying organ or tissue is unhealthy. This, too, should be brought to your vet's attention.

Massage is really a *complementary* form of health care for your dog. You have become your dog's first line of defense. It is not an alternative to competent veterinary care. As you can see, it works hand in paw with it.

> *Massage is not an alternative to competent veterinary care, it works hand and paw with it.*

Sides

Repeat sets of three strokes across both sides stroking with the grain of the hair. Start on the side of the muzzle, stroke under the ear, over

the side of the neck, over the shoulder, across the ribs, across the flank (hip) and to the side of the tail. Two slow, gentle, "Hi, how are you?"/ *Introduction* strokes and one deliberate *Assessment* stroke. Good.

Shoulder and Front Legs

The vertebra of the spine can be felt midway between the shoulder blades. Repeat the three passes from this midline place over the shoulder, and down each leg. Use Curved hands around the shoulder, gently pressing into the sides of the contour of the shoulder blade, feeling the muscles, tendons, long bones and joints.

Grounding

When stroking the front and hind legs, allow your hand to flow all the way down the leg, over the paw and onto the floor or carpet with two light passes. This  "grounding" stroke helps you bring your dog's attention down to the ground. It is just very nice for any of us to understand where we are and where we belong in this world. And right now, your dog has the pleasure of understanding that he/she belongs and can be comfortable on the ground.

On an energetic level you are helping your dog reinforce the connection to bio-electrical-magnetic forces of the earth, from which all life begins and ends and draws its power.

The third pass is firmer: assess for bruises, or tender areas. Note anything unusual and move on. You will return later to the areas that need special attention.

Now, repeat on the other side.

> *It is very nice for us to understand where we are and where we belong in this world.*

> *Your dog has the pleasure of understanding that he/she belongs...on the ground.*

Hind leg

Stroke from midline between the hips, covering the side, front and back of the upper leg, around and over the knee, down the inside 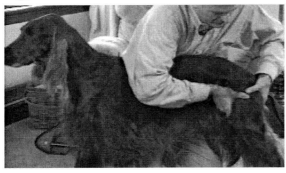 and outside of the lower leg (hock), over the paw and onto the ground. With your Curved Hands, wrap your fingers around the contours of the upper leg to include the inside of the thigh as you stroke down to the ground. Your thumbs will be sliding down the thigh from the hip to the knee. The first two passes are light, the third is slower and more deliberate. Again, press and feel the shapes of the contours of the underlying structures: sense the muscle groups, tendons and joints.

On the inside of the upper thigh, you'll feel a blood vessel running down from the groin. *DO NOT PRESS DIRECTLY ON THIS*, as it causes discomfort and numbness to the leg. Notice any soreness and/or stiffness. Are the muscles on one side the same size and shape as on the other side?

Now, repeat on other side.

The chest

Use the Open Hand to stroke from under the chin, down and across the neck and Curved Hand to move between the front legs to midline, the sternum (breastbone), and back to the belly. Remember, it is a three stroke set the third being the Assessment stroke. Note temperature, pulse, and breathing patterns both normal and unusual, and move on.

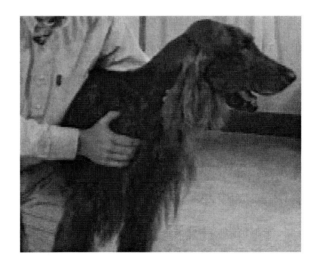

So far you have:

🦴 Allowed your dog to get used to your touch,

🦴 Become familiar with how your dog feels, and

🦴 Been able to identify possible areas that might need some extra TLC.

After you have practiced this section a few times, the "Introduction and Assessment" sequence should only last about 5 or 10 minutes.

This completes the first part of the massage. You're doing great.

Part 4 Therapeutic Massage Sequence

This is the part of the massage when you focus on areas requiring special treatment. The techniques and order of sections are all to be tailored you your dog's needs.

The face

Use Open Hand over the top, from the tip of the nose to the back of the skull. Feel for the little ridge or indentation that runs midline on the top center of the head. A dog's skull is made up of several bones which are joined together at suture lines, or joints which have formed between the borders of flat bones in the skull. This ridge is one of these suture lines.

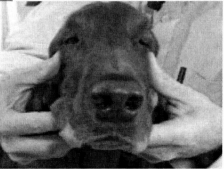

Gently compress as you Thumb walk along this line from just behind and between the eyes to the back of the skull. Press your thumbpads all across the back edge of the skull moving from behind one ear to behind the other ear.

Move back to the muzzle and with Curved Hands hold underneath the jowl and move your thumbs from midline on top, pressing in and down onto the flaps of the mouth. Place your fingers inside, between the flap of the mouth and the teeth. You 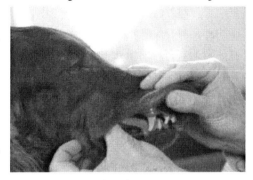 can rub the flaps of the mouth between your thumb and forefinger, then make little circular rubbing movements on the upper gums and lower gums all the way back and around.

Increasing circulation to the gums:

 Gets your dog used to someone working around his mouth,

helps your dog maintain healthy gums and teeth, and

 reduces unpleasant smelling breath.

If your dog resists work in or around his mouth, don't fight or try to force him; this is not a battle. Take a deep breath, relax and move on to the next part of the massage. Patience will pay off. As he becomes used to the concept that it's okay for your hands to be in his mouth, you'll be allowed do a little more each session. Soon he'll accept your hands and fingers graciously.

The eyes

The eyes, we've heard, are the windows to the soul. Take a deep breath, slowly and completely exhale as you Thumb Walk up and 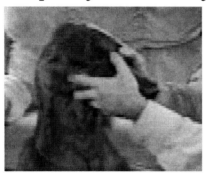 around the bony orbits of the eyes, working from the outside edges toward the midline and back underneath to the outsides. These are the hard oval edges of bone housing the eye sockets. You'll notice that your thumbs fall into very subtle little valleys as they move around the orbit of the eye.

Press gently around the outside of the edges of these ovals. Hold each press for 2 to 5 seconds, or until you sense the slightest feeling that the tissues are pushing your thumb away. This is called a "release." This may take some practice, but with patience, you will be able to feel the subtleties of massage.

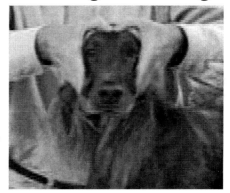

> *You'll notice your thumbs fall into subtle little valleys as they move around the orbit of the eye.*

Behind the orbit of the eyes are many sinus cavities. By gently pressing and encouraging them to release, you are helping them drain. This helps many sinus problems that are related to allergies or that could be the cause of runny noses and headaches.

One of the many benefits of learning the art of massage therapy is you learn to become much more sensitive in touching, feeling and understanding tiny nuances of nonverbal communication. You are now learning to sense tiny bio-electrical power surges in your dog's face!

Just above and to the sides of the eyes you'll feel a soft oval area. This is the temporal area. Use your thumbs or fingers to gently rub this area in little circles. Watch your dog's eyes as you massage away the cares and troubles of the world. Nice, very nice.

You are learning to sense tiny bio-electrical power surges in your dog's face!

Allow me to share a story from my experience. I was teaching a caregiver to feel for the notches on his ancient dog's spine. No matter how "soft" he made his hands, he was not able to sense them. I suggested he pretend to feel them, thereby giving himself permission to expand his awareness. And just like that, he *got* it. We all felt a quiet stillness in the room and caught our breaths when the *Old Boy* turned to look up at us with big shining eyes, sighed and softly laid his head down on his paws.-JR

The ears

Thumb Walk up the bony ridge and back to the ears, and use Curved Hands around the

sides of the head. Hold the sides of the head in your palms. Thumb Walk compression all around the soft area at the base of the ears. Fold each ear in half (the long way) and pull off from the base outward toward the tip.

When you get to the outer tip of the ear, give it a hard squeeze. This is an acupressure "shock" point. Applying pressure to it is a very effective way to increase circulation to the entire nervous system. Giving it a good squeeze at this point in the massage is giving your dog a refreshing tonic.

> ## *Giving a good squeeze to the tip of the ear is giving your dog a refreshing tonic.*

Completion of the head

Gently *tap* across the top of the head with the pads of the fingers of your Open Hand. This balances and redistributes the cerebral spinal fluid within the skull

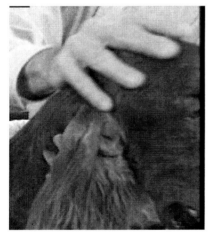

cavity that surrounds and cushions the brain. With the pads of your fingertips (Curved Hand), *tap* across the back edge of the skull. This softens and relaxes the muscle attachment sites on the back of the neck.

Be sure to keep your hands relaxed and loose. All movement should be from (flapping) the wrist. Tap your own head and neck with your fingertips for 15 seconds. It's very refreshing. Smooth the entire head with quick, gentle, yet firm effleurage strokes before moving on to the...

Neck and upper spine

Thumb Walk down the neck from the back of the skull to the shoulder blades slowly pressing into the little soft valleys between the bones of the neck (vertebrae) on either side of the spine. The direction for the pressure is first directly into the valleys and then crowd your fingers up into the next vertebra toward the head.

CAUTION:
DO NOT PRESS DIRECTLY ONTO THE SPINE.
Too much pressure could cause injury.

Work this area thoroughly. Grab a handful of coat on both sides of the neck and give it a strong shake. This greatly stimulates the neck muscles used for head carriage and helps loosen the muscles in the shoulder. Finish this area using Curved Hand S*moothing* strokes down the sides of the neck to the top of the chest.

> **Take care not to press directly onto the top of the spine; too much pressure here could cause injury.**

The spine, ribs and abdomen

Notice that the shapes of the bones in the spine change just in front of the shoulder. These bones in the spine attach to the ribs. The ribs are the protective armor or cage housing the heart, the lungs and other important organs. We can stimulate these internal organs by gently pressing into the valleys, spaces between the ribs right up next to the spine.

Start against the spine (but NOT ON the spine) and crowd your fingers up into the spine and angle them in the direction of the head. Gently press, hold and release.

One way your dog lets you know that you are using too much pressure is, he will tense his back muscles to guard against possible injury. Do not use too much pressure, it is abusive and causes discomfort.

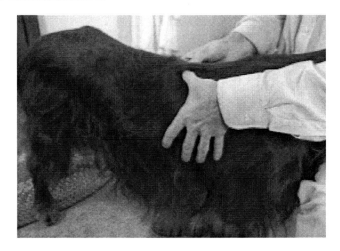

Run your fingers down the spine between the ridges of the rib cage, following the curve of

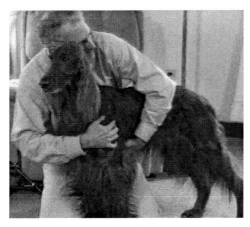

the ribs to the sternum (bottom midline). Lift your working hand, and move it 2 inches further back (toward the tail) on the spine and repeat, following the natural curve of the body down to the sternum.

Abdominal lift

After you have completed all the grooves between the ribs reach under your dog (who needs to be standing for this movement), clasp your hands together and slowly and gently lift the upper abdomen. This is the soft area just below the ribs. Hold for the count of 1-2-3 and gently and slowly lower and release. Move your hands a couple of inches further back and repeat. Clasp your hands, lift for the count of 3 and slowly lower.

This technique takes pressure off the spine/top-line when you pull up. The gentle compression supports the diaphragm, the primary breathing muscle, aids the peristaltic movement of the intestines and enhances the whole process of elimination.

Come back up to the spinal column and continue to press, hold and release the

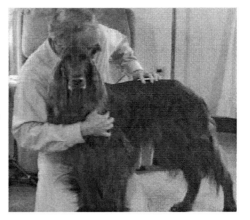

remainder of the spaces between the vertebrae all the way back to the tail. Acupressure points are always in the valleys. By stimulating this series of points on your dog's back you are helping him to balance the movement of fluids throughout his body.

> *Actually, after you have completed an*
> *entire massage, you will have touched*
> *on almost all of the 40 major*
> *acupressure points on your dog's body.*

Compression and joint movement to limbs

Forelimb and paw

You've worked the head, neck, spine, and ribs. Now return to the shoulders. Supporting the

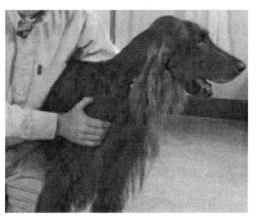

body of your dog against your body or with one hand, curl your other hand around the upper leg, your fingers pressing into the roundness of the muscles of the chest. This is an area that receives a lot of strain, especially in very active dogs. Your dog will tell you if extra therapy is desired here by leaning the weight of his body into your hand. Massage can really loosen tight muscles.

> *Your dog will tell you if extra therapy is desired by leaning the weight of his body into your hand.*

Compress the muscles and tendons onto the underlying bones. Use both hands in curved position to feel for the contours of the upper shoulder and gently squeeze. 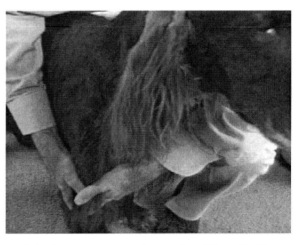 Imagine you are slowly squeezing half of the water out of a wet sponge and when you release your pressure, the sponge fills up again with pure fresh water.

This is exactly what is happening to the muscles you are compressing. You are squeezing out the old blood and lymph, providing space and low pressure to draw in and bathe the cells of the muscles in fresh, richly oxygenated blood. Blood normally flows around passive muscles and through active ones. By compressing the muscles you are helping them be active. This helps increase circulation to the entire body. You can see how beneficial this is!

As you move down from the shoulder to the upper leg, holding and squeezing, feel for knots, tightness, hardened areas that may be 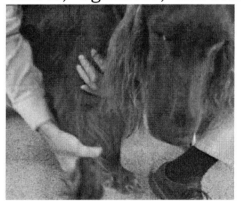 within the long muscle fibers. When you sense each one, gently rub across the spot in little circles. This is called cross fiber massage. You will soon feel the knot "dissolve" beneath your fingers. Before moving on, hold the spot with a *very light* touch (about the weight of a nickel) for a few seconds to "set" the softening experience.

Continue squeezing and releasing as you move systematically down the leg to the knee. When your hand is on the knee, grasp it, bend it, lift it and rotate the joint at the shoulder in small circles, three times in each direction. This area does not have a lot of flexibility in lateral movement, so make your movements gentle.

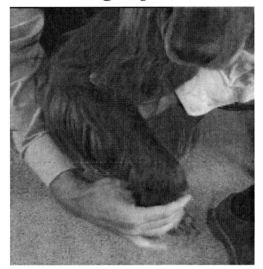

Flex and extend the knee, which only moves back and forth—NOT IN CIRCLES. Move down to the paw. Flex and extend, back and forth.

Stretch the base of the paw by pressing your finger in between the pads. Press up against the sides of each of the pads and rub the skin in-between. The pressure can be either gentle or more vigorous; either will be effective. There are many acupressure points here and on the bases of the pads. Stimulating them in this way is especially invigorating to the internal organs of the body.

Smooth with integrating strokes from shoulder to paws and repeat on the other leg.

Remember to breathe, slowly and easily. Feel your abdomen expanding when you inhale and relaxing inward as your lungs empty. This keeps you relaxed and focused. Your dog is acutely aware of and responsive to your level of anxiety or relaxation.

> *Your dog is acutely aware of and responsive to your level of anxiety or relaxation.*

Hind limb and paw

Move to the hip area. If your dog is standing, support his body against your own and reach over to hold the hip on the other (opposite) side with both hands; one in front, the other in back. If your dog is lying on his side, the upper leg will be easy to reach. Then, to work the other side, you'll just have to turn him over.

With Curved hands, compress along the contours of the upper leg, sensing for muscle tightness. Include the hamstring muscle on the back of the thigh. Run the tips of your fingers up from the back of the knee to the seat bone *against* the lay of the 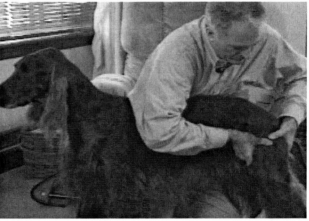 hair pressing with enough pressure to make a furrow in the hair. If you feel any knots, slowly rub them out with your thumb and forefinger. You can either move up the length of the muscle following the direction of the fibers, or side to side across the belly of the muscle, cross fiber. Often, simply holding the pads of your fingers on the knot is enough to soften it.

Repeat. Work your fingers into the muscled area around the hip joint, feeling for the shapes of the bones where they meet.

Supporting the hip with one hand, grasp and gently bend the knee, lifting the paw off the surface. Rotate the leg from the hip joint in small circles three times in each direction. Move down to flex and extend the paw moving it back and forth, again, three times.

Spread the pads, stretching and expanding the width of the paw. Take special notice of possible cuts, ice, matted hair, or debris, which might be trapped between the pads; each of which could be the cause of discomfort and potentially, infection. Assess, assess.

Press your fingers in between the pads of the paws and press all around the sides of the pads and the sensitive skin between them. Smooth down the leg with integrating strokes and repeat on the other hip.

The tail

There are up to 23 bones in the tail, so it is a significant extension of the spine. Gently compress between the bones all the way from the base of the tail to its tip. This is done with one hand working methodically down the entire

length, as the other hand supports the body over the hip. Move your hands so that you can support the base of the tail with one hand and curl the part of the tail closest to the body up into a question mark. Slowly rotate the tail first in one direction, then in the other.

Grasp the tail at the base, lift it and place your other hand at the base of the neck and give a gentle spinal stretch.

Your dog will really enjoy this!

DNA, or genetic memory is very important in your dog's self concept. When we massage a part that is missing, such as a bobbed tail, cropped ears, or an amputated limb, work the whole part, as if it were still there. That is the way your dog remembers it to be. When he was born, his body was completely intact, without any of the scars of physical or emotional trauma he would eventually incur. That is the way your dog remembers it to be. Skip this part, and the massage is incomplete. It's imperative to massage the *whole* body.

Dogs, like humans also may experience the phenomenon of phantom pain in their missing limbs. Massage has been shown to be extremely effective in alleviating this very real discomfort. When holding a dysplastic hip, for example, stimulate it, and bring your dog's attention to this specific spot. By triggering his memory; his *genetic* memory, you can support his effort to re-achieve his ideal memory of a healthy, whole part.

> **When we massage a part that is missing, such as a bobbed tail, cropped ears, or amputated limb, we work the whole part, as if it were still there.**

Completing the massage

You have now worked the head, neck and upper spine, spine, ribs, abdomen, shoulders, front legs and paws, hip, hind legs, rear paws, and tail. We'll now use an abbreviated version of the Introduction and Assessment part of the massage, but now, with only 2 passes in each set. The first is a slow, deliberate Assessment stroke, the second is a final gentle and flowing, Smoothing, or integrating, stroke. Please note that this order is the reverse of the beginning; balancing the first part of the massage.

> ***Finish with grounding strokes down each of the legs.***

Start across the top line, stroking from the top of the head, over the spine, to the tip of the tail. Assess and smooth around the face, neck and chest. Move down the sides from midline above (spine) to midline below (sternum and abdomen), following the curvature of the ribs. Allow your hands to flow from the shoulders down the forelegs, over the paws and to the ground. Assess and smooth from the hips, down the hind legs, over the paws and to the ground.

Note any changes you feel in your dog's body. You may want to take notice of *your* attitude as well; are you calm and relaxed?

Your dog has had quite a workout, so a good nap is in order. He'll need this because the compression and stimulation of his muscles and other tissues has been very aerobic. Also, the benefits of massage are not always apparent right away. Your dog may be a little stiff for several hours, especially if the massage was a lot more rigorous than his normal level of activity. The effects of a thorough massage often are not completely integrated for a couple of days. But, you've done your job, and he'll do his; to heal himself and feel better.

This geriatric Doberman went from complete disability to unassisted walking and playing—all from healing massage. (Blitzer)

Part 5 Older Dog

How they are different

In the first chapter, we learned the basic strokes, hand positions, pressures and a routine. You now have the skills to give a good canine massage. Now we'll take a look at older dogs, who they are, their ailments and what we can do to help them in their reclining and declining years.

In this section, you will learn techniques used in a more vigorous, stimulating massage. You will become acquainted with some acupressure points, Positional Release, Exploration of Movement and "healing touch," a type of off-the-body work. Your expertise and awareness of useful methods will be expanded, giving you more ways to help your aging dog cope with the difficulties of growing older and infirm.

> *Your expertise and awareness of useful methods will be expanded...*
> *to help your aging dog.*

As dogs age, their likelihood of becoming ill or injured increases. You want to make your pet comfortable in his geriatric years without expensive medications and surgeries. Massage therapy is a skill both you and your dog will truly appreciate. Massaging dogs doesn't need gadgets, specialized tools, mats or fragranced accessories. All it needs is a giver (you), a receiver (your dog), a quiet place and the easily learned skills in this manual.

> *Massage therapy for dogs doesn't need gadgets, specialized tools, mats or fragranced accessories.*

In *Four Paws, Five Directions*, author Dr. Cheryl Schwartz writes that physical touch can heal by increasing circulation of blood, lymph and "energy flow."

By "energy flow" we refer to the spark of life force that moves within and

> *Dogs who lay for long periods and generally lack exercise will benefit from the aerobic qualities of massage.*

around you and your dog's body. In India, it's called *Prana*, and is considered that aspect of the eternal in our temporal bodies. In China, it's called *Ch'i*. Its movement and flow patterns have been documented as Meridians and used as reference points in acupressure, acupuncture, and Ch'i Gung healing. In the West, it's called *The Holy Spirit*, or *Life Force*.

Whatever its name, its existence has been universally accepted by every human culture. And, although not well understood, its movement and flow have been used in techniques of hands-on healing since the dawn of history.

We understand the importance of blood flow. Lymph, however, may not be part of your everyday vocabulary, but it is important.

Lymph is a clear fluid that carries your white blood cells. White blood cells kill germs, fight infections and remove the used up cells from your tissues. This is the foundation and mechanism of your immune system. We must have our lymph circulating and available whenever and wherever it is needed.

Lymph doesn't have a pump, as the blood has the heart, to move it around the body. It has been described as a stagnant pool of water, which needs to be manually squeezed for circulation. Normally, lymph is moved about by the pumping action of muscles as they compress against each other in movement, happening most effectively at the major joints. You'll find large lymph nodes behind the jaws, under the front legs and in the groin. Sometimes the nodes, or storage pockets of lymphatic fluid and cells stop up and become stuck, swollen, or inflamed. Massage helps reestablish normal flow and drainage.

Benefits of massage for your older dog:

Maintains body tone and flexibility.

Relieves pain/discomfort naturally without the use of drugs.

Continuous hands on assessment of both physical and emotional conditions.

Complements veterinary treatments.

Speeds healing process.

Aids emotional adjustment process.

Pre and post surgery speeds healing process and decreases atrophy of muscle tissue.

Modifies inappropriate behaviors caused by the anxiety and depression brought on by physical and emotional stressors,

- physical-- awareness of declining abilities to perform normal dog activities, and

- emotional-- separation from companions or changes in family circumstances.

Effects of Aging Process
Older dogs

A number of things happen in their bodies as dogs age. The first things we notice are the skin and the coat. The skin becomes dryer, loses its elasticity and begins to sag. The hair around the muzzle grays and the coat becomes dull as hair follicles take up less nutrients. Internal organs become less efficient, causing them to work harder just to keep functioning. The muscles, tendons and ligaments become stiff having lost much of their suppleness and elastic quality.

Joints, whose surfaces become irritated and worn due to reduced lubrication, develop calcium deposits. Bone against bone grinding makes it more painful for your dog to move, so he/she reduces his/her exercise level. Without natural movement, the digestive system becomes more sluggish as evidenced by bowel movement changes. Old cells lose the ability to replace themselves with new cells when they wear out. So it seems as if we are watching a system as it breaks down.

> **Massage can be used as a partial substitute for exercise because it maintains and increases circulation and flexibility.**

The kindest thing about the aging process is that it happens *gradually*. We may find ourselves carrying them more, lifting them into the car or up or down steps. We shorten our walks, allowing time for rest. We make sure their aged bodies stay warm by keeping them out of drafts and rubbing them to increase circulation when they are chilled.

We can help them maintain their flexibility to the last by aiding them with joint movement exercises. A brief massage gives your dog a complete aerobic workout. So much so that he will most likely want to nap afterward.

Many behavioral changes are due to the aging process. Reduced vision may cause someone to walk into furniture. Hearing loss is evident when there's no response the first time you call. Slower movements and discomfort or weakness in joints may be signs of bursitis.

Bursitis is inflammation of the sacs of lubricating fluid which cushion and ease the movement of bones against each other in joints.

There is reduced elasticity of *connective tissue,* the living tissue fabric that weaves between the skin and bone, fat and muscles, and surrounding each of the muscle fibers within each of the muscle bundles. (An example of connective tissue would be the thin membrane between the skin and the meat of a chicken.)

It's easy to understand how the normal metabolism and movement of the body loses its oomph, when connective tissue becomes dryer and less elastic. The benefits of massage, increased circulation and vitality are evident in all tissues: bones, tendons, ligaments, muscles and skin.

Actually, massage can be used as a partial substitute for exercise because it maintains and increases circulation and flexibility. Dogs who lay for long periods and generally lack exercise will benefit from the aerobic qualities of massage.

Older dogs with reduced activity levels may develop pressure sores on bony area where there is a lack of circulation. The primary locations for pressure spots on dogs are behind the knees, the hocks and the front elbows. Pay close attention to affected areas for they could soon become open sores and sites for infection. Rather than avoid them, and passively allow them to repair themselves in their own time, use massage to encourage circulation around, over, and through sore spots.

> *Rather than avoiding sore spots, massage around, over, and through them.*

Prevention could also be in the form of a soft mat or sheepskin, which will protect compromised areas where constant pressure reduces revitalizing blood flow.

Older dog massage

Although care must be taken not to use too much force on old bones, older dogs especially benefit when various vigorous strokes that are more stimulating are incorporated into their massage.

Part 1: Use the same Introduction and Assessment strokes already described to warm and gently stretch the muscles, as before any exercise session.

Part 2: Next, as you move on to the working/therapy part of the massage, you'll include the techniques of:
vibration,
joint movement/range of motion,
skin rolling,
tapping

These are all helpful to encourage circulation and an enhanced sense of well-being. These will help your dog to really feel great!

Introduction and Assessment strokes warm and gently stretch the muscles.

The head

As a dog matures some of the most noticeable changes occur on the face. The area around the front of the muzzle turns a distinguished gray, the jowls tend to become a little looser, and the skin around the eyes and on the forehead becomes more wrinkled.

The head, including the muzzle, eyes and ears are among the most sensitive and therefore vulnerable areas on your dog's body.

The mouth and nose were the first parts used for sensing. When only a tiny puppy long before eyes were opened, these organs were identifying scents, assessing shapes, sizes, textures and tastes of unfamiliar (and unusual) objects. There is actually a second organ used for the sense of smell, located in the mouth behind the front teeth. This additional organ helps dogs track scents that are weeks old, or that have been covered by snow.

The area around the mouth has been identified as *referencing* to the Limbic System, the part of the brain that deals with emotion. A lot of memories are associated with experiences and objects, which have been involved one way or another with and/or in your dog's mouth. It is, of course, also for eating, chewing, grooming, and playing. We will be working around the mouth, the muzzle, and on the gums to increase circulation and reduce tension. This will also help if your dog's breath isn't always "springtime fresh."

The eyes are also vulnerable areas. As your dog ages, he may have problems similar to those that afflict humans, such as glaucoma. At any age, he may suffer from the symptoms of allergies, such as, weepy irritated eyes. It is very important to massage around the eyes. In the process, you'll maintain a close observation, you'll increase circulation, aid sinus and lymphatic drainage. You'll also rebalance the lines of energy, which begin at the head and flow throughout the body. This is very important in maintaining and restoring healthfulness.

There are eye muscle strengthening exercises you may want to incorporate into your massage session. One is to hold your dog's head in a fixed position with one hand while moving a toy around in front of him with the other. Allow his eyes to track the toy as you move it to 9 O'clock, then to 3 O'clock, to 6, to 12, then slowly clockwise all the way around to 12. Then move it counterclockwise all the way back to 12. This strengthens all eye movement muscles.

Another is to hold the toy close to his face and direct his attention (and vision) to an object across the room. Repeat. This strengthens muscles used in focusing. The entire sequence may be more than his attention span can handle but do as much as you can. Your dog's vision (and attention span) will be enhanced.

Dogs use up to seventeen muscles to move each of their ears. Important as tools of communication, they are receivers that can be swiveled to get the best reception, or twitched to flick away annoying insects or pests. Their attitude, angle and direction play a significant part of the body language used to communicate with people and other dogs. So, we'll pay particular attention to them.

While you are massaging the ears, fold them back to examine for debris or mites. This is the assessment and health maintenance aspect of massage. There are also, many acupressure points on and around the ears. Be sure to massage the whole ear, and beyond, if part of it has been cut, or torn.

The order we'll use in massaging the head is:
    eyes and temporal area,
    base of the ears,
    flaps of the ears and tips,
    sides of the jaw,
    muzzle,
    gums,
    and top of the skull.

Use one hand to support the dog's head as you begin to apply compression in the temporal area on either side of the skull. Small circles of compression with your fingertips work best around the eyes and up the snout. Apply compression with a Curved Hand around his head area. Gently compress the sinus cavities around the eyes.

Massage the snout and work your fingers inside the flap of skin between the teeth and the mouth. Stretch the flap between thumb and fingers moving all around the mouth. Massage the gums. This will get him used to work being done in his mouth and may be helpful in other applications.

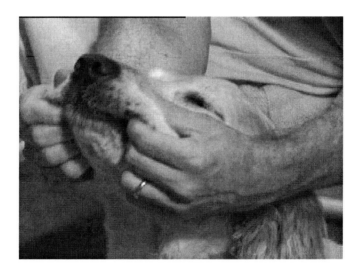

Rub and stretch the skin under the muzzle, the *dewlap*.

Move back under the ears, and work your fingers up pressing into the little hollows all around the base of the ears. Support the base of the ear with one hand, fold it in half with the other and firmly stroke off the length of the ear and off the tip. This stimulates the acupressure points at the base of the ears and balances the flow of fluids as well as air pressures within the ear canals.

Support the bottom of the jaw with one hand and firmly stroke the top of the skull, following the lay of the hair, from just above the eyes to the back edge of the head.

Smooth the entire face and head. Be aware of the tone and texture of your voice. It is an important element of your massage session. Remember to keep breathing.

Be aware of the tone and texture of your voice. It is an important element of your massage session.

Part 6 The upper spine and back
(Included with Older Dog Massage)

The upper spine is the cervical (neck) area from the back of the skull to the center between the shoulder blades. Increasing circulation here is helpful when there is tightness in the shoulders, overused muscles, or arthritis. If muscles spasm in this area, the flow of blood to the nerves of the legs may be impeded, resulting in numbness.

> *The flow of blood to the nerves of the legs may be impeded, resulting in numbness.*

Support the head from under the chin with one hand as you use your thumb and fingers of the other hand to compress on either side of the spine. There are two ways to affect the area, deep tissue massage and positional release.

The first is to slowly press into the muscle tissue, moving deeper as the tissue softens and accepts your touch. Angle your pressure into the hollows between the vertebrae, and allow the tips of your thumbs and fingers to be pulled up toward the head as you press in.

> ### *Soften the muscles bordering the spine.*

Balance each stroke so that your exit from the tissue is at the same rate as your entrance. This can become very deep work, so it is imperative that your entrances and exits are gentle and compassionate. Press into each of the hollows as you work down to where the shapes of the bones in the spine change.

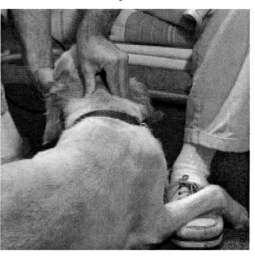

Another technique, which is also extremely effective, is called *positional release*. This involves the use of *very* light touch. While supporting the head from underneath the jowl, softly hold your other thumb and middle finger to just under the back of the head against and on both sides of the spine. Cradle the uppermost vertebrae that you can feel with a touch so light that your fingers barely graze the top of the coat. Hold your hands in this position. In a short while, your hands will slowly move slightly to one side and then back. As this movement occurs, and as muscle tightness is released, you may feel a little pulse under your fingers. Your dog is making tiny skeletal self-adjustments!

> ### *Your dog is making tiny skeletal self-adjustments!*

This takes some practice. You may not feel it the first time. Please be patient with yourself. Massage is a skill that becomes more effective as you practice.

Use compression in small circles on both sides of the spine with your thumbs starting at the shoulders working all the way down to the base of the tail. Feel the muscles and the spaces between them. Feel for fatty areas, cysts, and hot and cold spots. Hot spots may indicate an infected area. Cold spots indicate sites of previous injuries.

If your dog indicates there is a feeling of discomfort as you rub on the lower back, above the haunches, this could be a symptom of kidney irritation, so consult with your vet.

The tail

As you support the body placing one hand on the lower part of the spine, just in front of the tail, grasp the part of the tail closest to the body and curl it over so that the tip of the tail points to the ground. Hold it up so that it is higher than the line of the spine. Rotate the tail in little circles a couple of times in both directions.

As you move your hand down the length of the tail, close your hand gently over each of the joints. Smooth with a steady firm stroke from hip to tip of tail and beyond. There are as many as 23 bones in the tail. So, it's a significant continuation of the spine.

> ### There are as many as 23 bones in the tail.

The back

Next, use *vibration,* on both sides of the spine from shoulders to hips. Rest your hand or outstretched fingers firmly on his coat, so that your touch is affecting the connective tissue beneath the skin. Remember to maintain contact also with the supporting hand. Shake your hand rapidly while pressing in. You can use both hands, placing fingers in the grooves between the ribs to vibrate the hands down the sides. Move back on the spine a hand-width and repeat. Wake up and stimulate the whole body this way; it's a great energizing tonic. Integrate with Smoothing strokes

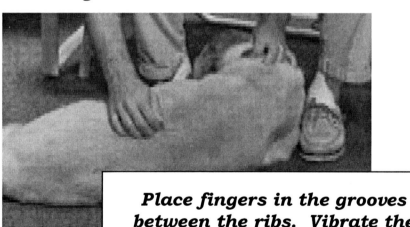

Place fingers in the grooves between the ribs. Vibrate the hands down the sides.

Return to the neck and grab a handful of coat on both sides of the shoulders. Pull the skin up away from the body, stretching it up and rolling it between your fingers and palms. Then, release it to contract back to the body. Roll the skin all across the shoulders, over the back, and over the hips. As dogs (and people) age, their skin loses much of its elasticity. Skin rolling helps maintain youthful resiliency.

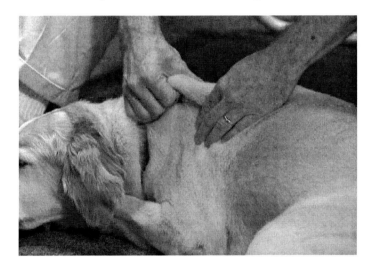

Skin rolling helps maintain youthful resiliency.

The hind legs

As you work across each of the hips, lift the hind leg gently away from the line of the body and move the limb in small circles, first one direction and reversing, the other way. Support the upper part of the leg with one hand and flex and extend the other joints in the leg.

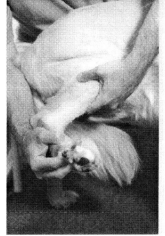

Move down the legs compressing into the sides. Press all around each of the pads on the paws. Again, you are stimulating many acupressure spots.

It is not really necessary to know the exact effects of touching specific spots. By the time you have finished a complete massage session, you will have covered many of the referral points necessary to balance the body.

Repeat on the other leg. Smooth from the hips down the legs.

Compress into the sides all around each of the pads on the paws stimulating many acupressure spots.

Front legs and shoulders

Move up and repeat on front shoulders. Compress the large muscle groups above, inside and outside the shoulder joint. Joint movement of the shoulders helps loosen and relax the muscles used in the head carriage. Flex and extend the joints of the front legs. Compress around the pads of the front paws. Smooth from the shoulders down to the paws.

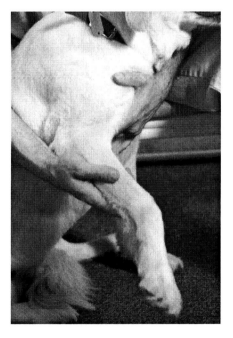

Completion

Return to the neck, take hold of either side of the coat and give it a good brisk shake. Move up to the head, support the jaw with one hand, and gently tap the top of the skull rapidly with your extended fingers. This stimulates and rebalances *cerebral spinal fluid* and opens the sinuses. Finish with overall Smoothing strokes. Allow your hands, when smoothing down the legs, to flow all the way to the ground.

> ***Gently tap the top of the skull rapidly with the pads of your extended fingers.***

Part 7 Respiratory enhancement

Certain breeds of dogs are more susceptible to respiratory problems. Boxers, Bulldogs, and Shih Tzus, for example, have little tortured nasal tracts, that affect air intake and sinuses. Massage can greatly enhance their ability to breathe. Actually, this type of massage is helpful for all dogs in that it supports the breathing mechanics and increases the generalized oxygenation of all tissues.

Be sure to use the Introduction and Assessment sequence over the entire body to warm and soften the muscles you will be working.

Support the head in your hands as you thoroughly massage around the muzzle, orbits of the eyes, and on either side of the ridge on the top of the skull. Use the pad of the thumb, not the tip and the nail, as you Thumb Walk. You'll have more sensitivity to feeling and you'll prevent intensive pressure.

> **Use the pad of the thumb, not the tip of the nail. You'll prevent pressure that's too intense.**

Using your whole hand, pinch the back of the neck. Hold for the count of 3 and release. This helps widen the nasal tracts and opens sinuses so they can drain.

Under the jowl, stroke down the throatlatch, on either side of the trachea, or windpipe (NOT ON IT) to the sternum breastbone). Using circular  movements with the pads of your fingertips, massage the chest. You are increasing circulation and warming the deltoids (muscles on the front of the shoulder), pectoral muscles (just inside and behind the forelegs) and the intercostals (between the ribs) on the sides of the sternum (breastbone). These are the Accessory breathing muscles that help the chest expand and contract.

Use gentle compression as you sweep your fingers between the ribs from the spine on the topline around to the sternum where the ribs attach. Press gently into the hollows felt along the sternum between the ribs as this area may be sensitive. Press up toward the head and the heart.

Chest compression

Support one side of the body with one hand and hold the ribs behind the opposite shoulder with the other. Compress the ribcage allowing your working hand to gently press towards the supporting hand. Squeeze out the old stale air.

As you release your pressure, the lungs fill back up with lots of new fresh air. Repeat on the other side.

> **Allow your working hand to gently press towards the supporting hand.**

Curl your fingers over the front of the shoulders. Rotate the shoulders in small, slow circles. Hold, squeeze, and gently pump rhythmically at a pace of about one every three seconds.

You are increasing circulation to many of the muscles used for respiration, draining the lymph nodes (submandibular, pre-scapular and axillary) behind the shoulders and under the jowl. This encourages the filtration and flow of white blood cells, the internal disease fighters. Your dog's inside will breathe easier with the welcome assistance from you on the outside.

> **Your dog's insides will breathe easier with the welcome assistance from _you_ on the outside.**

Part 8 Hips

Hips are large joints that are the site of a lot of stress especially during times of growth and times of senior citizen mobility. Hips have dysplasia when the ball of the femur (long bone of the hind leg) cannot make full solid contact when it moves within the hip joint. This can be the result of injury, arthritis, or inheritance. Although deep massage of this area may be uncomfortable for the dog, it is essential in the healing process. For a dog with hip problems, this could be the most effective therapy to help him/her regain strength and activity in the hip.

> ***This could be the most effective therapy to help him/her regain strength and activity in the hip.***

Dogs genetically predisposed to hip problems also benefit. Regularly scheduled massage sessions maintain healthy joints as well as encourage the repair of damaged ones.

Begin with the Introduction and Assessment sequence covering the entire body.

This will prepare your dog for the more specific work on the hip.

Inside of the thigh

Cup your hand on the inside of your dog's rear leg. Use Compression with your fingertips in little circles to warm and soften the muscles high up into the groin.  You may be able to feel a blood vessel here. If so, move off to its side, continuing the little circles up and down the inside of the thigh on both sides of the vessel.

If at any time you feel trembling or internal shaking, ease off on the pressure you are using. Please note that you keep seeing the words *softly* and *gently*. It is never necessary to push hard, to go deep. You need barely touch the surface to affect muscles and systems deep within.

> **If at any time you feel trembling or internal shaking, reduce your pressure.**

Should you locate a tight knot of muscle, gently rub your finger across the width of the knot. This is *cross fiber* stroking. You can also softly hold your finger on the (*trigger point*) spot while you take a deep, relaxing breath. This, too, is very effective in dispersing muscular tension.

Outside the thigh

Locate and feel about the contours of the outside of the hip joint. Warm and gently stretch the muscles compressing the tissues using circular movements with your fingers and/or the heel of your palm. Continue down the leg, warming the muscles, ligaments and tendons, flexing and extending each joint, moving it back and forth to the paw. Gently insert your forefinger into the spaces between the pads; spread out the paw. You are opening channels so energy can flow.

> ***Gently stretch and warm the muscles.***

Exploration of movement of the hip

Support the dog's body with one hand under his abdomen. With your other hand, pick up the leg and slightly move it away from the body. Move the leg in slow circles from the hip. Slowly move the upper long leg bone away from the midline. Slowly and gently compress it back

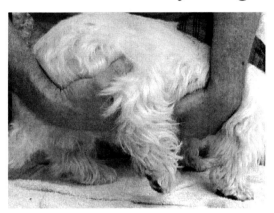

into the hip joint. Support it in this position and wait for 5-10 seconds or until the leg begins to move on its own.

> *Support it in this position until the leg begins to move on its own.*

Sense the movements and allow the dog to explore his own range of comfort while you cradle the limb in your hand. Which way feels better? Which way feels worse? This is called *exploration of movement*. When you feel the leg has completed its movement, usually taking less than 30 seconds, pause to hold and support the final position. Pause again, this time to take in a deep breath. Slowly exhale. Pay attention to your dog's breathing, too. Then, gently lower the paw back to the ground.

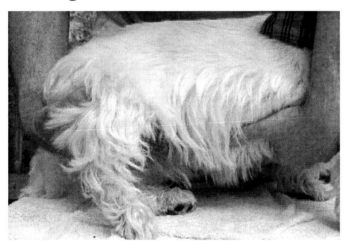

Complete with *smoothing* strokes from hip to paw to ground the energy, integrating and "setting" the therapeutic improvement. After just a few sessions, you will notice a difference in your dog's gait, ease of movement, and sense of peacefulness when quietly lying down.

Part 9 Additional techniques

Acupressure

An acupressure point is a spot on the body that is a direct link to energy flow through the internal organ systems. When stimulated, it triggers the release of the body's own naturally produced opiates, or painkillers.

There are approximately 40 major acupressure points on your dog's body. The paths of these points are the many meridians, or channels of energy flow throughout the body. Holding your finger on one or several of these points in succession helps balance systems, which may be hyperactive, or sluggish.

> *There are approximately 40 major acupressure points on your dog's body.*

A thorough account of these points, their actions, and specifics of meridian routes is beyond the scope of this manual. (See: *Four*

Paws, Five Directions, References/Further Reading.) But, they are located primarily around and on the tips of the ears, along the jaw line, between ribs and vertebrae, and on the insides and the outsides of the limbs.

They are always located in "valleys," or slight depressions on the body, i.e., between the pads on the paws, and above the eyes. So, if any place you touch you sense a slight depression, you are more than likely affecting internal body systems via an acupressure pathway.

As you learn to trust the intuitive movements of your fingers, you'll begin to allow them to linger, to hold, and to gently encourage very subtle variances in energy flow.

> ***Gently encourage very subtle variances in energy flow.***

Healing through visualization with therapeutic healing touch

Visualize yourself in a beautiful and calm setting. Find yourself in that place and breathe slowly and quietly as you observe yourself experiencing the peace. Allow your hand to rest gently on the traumatized area of your dog, holding his attention to that spot. Pause to release your expectations. Healing on this level cannot be hurried or forced. The same peace, contentment, feeling of safety and wholeness that you experience will be felt by your friend on the spot where your hand rests.

*Healing on this level
cannot be hurried or forced.*

Off-the-body massage

Off-the-body work is important for areas recently injured or for those with cancer, tumors or cysts. Open wounds or fractures, which have not yet knitted, are not appropriate for contact massage. Cancers, tumors or cysts are encapsulated; direct massage may rupture the capsule, allowing the toxic contents to leak, compromising other parts of the body. So, because you can't, or don't want to massage directly on the affected areas, you may need to work *off-the-body.* One way to work off-, or away from the body is by observing and working with the primary energy shells.

Energy shells

Energy shells are layers of energy surrounding your dog, like additional coats. Place your hand lightly on his body; feel his energy. Feel the softness and warmth radiating from within him. Move your hand only a half-inch off his body. You still feel the warmth; this is the shell closest to the physical body, the **etheric** layer.

> **Feel the softness and warmth radiating from within him.**

Move your hand an inch and a half off the body and feel the **emotional** shell. This is the one which would be more affected by emotional upheaval such as moving to a new neighborhood or when family dynamics change, i.e., when a child leaves home for school or a family becomes unglued during a divorce.

Dogs are often overwhelmed by grief when someone, either a human companion, or another family pet, has died. Historical accounts note that when Queen Marie Antoinette of France was executed by guillotine in 1793, her pet spaniel, Thisbe, was so depressed that she leaped into the River Seine and drowned.

Dogs do grieve; their feelings run deep and their memories last long. Massage is a way to help both of you through the most challenging times.

> **When Queen Marie Antoinette was executed by guillotine in 1793, her pet spaniel, Thisbe, was so depressed that she leaped into the River Seine and drowned.**

Move your hand 3-4 inches off the body and feel the **mental** *shell*. This is where your dog's self concept can be assisted. Your dog has memories of an active, happy life. Watch him happily race after his prey as he sleeps. He is also very much aware of present difficulties and disabilities. When the two no longer match, your dog may need some support in coping with the disparity. You can assist him, incorporating off-the-body techniques into your physical massage.

> ***Watch him happily race after his prey as he sleeps.***

Working with energy shells

These shells--or layers--are not solid. They are energy. They mingle and overlap. Each affects and is affected by the other (and additional) shells. If your dog has a physical injury or disease, hold your hand above the affected area at the height that you intuitively determine is appropriate.

Relax, close your eyes, and breathe in quiet meditation, until you feel your hand being gently pulled closer or pushed away. This is your dog's body communicating with you. He is either accepting your bio-electrical-magnetic boost, or is overstimulated and needs his space to heal.

Sometimes he/she may need to heal himself in his own "shell-cave." This is reason enough to remember that it is important to ask for and get permission before administering massage. Smooth stroke over the entire body through that field and again through the lower fields. Lastly, use light touch-*smoothing* strokes on your dog's physical body.

You will notice a difference in your dog's gait, ease of movement, and sense of peacefulness when quietly lying down.

Part 10 Summary

In this manual, we've explored and learned the basic pet massage for dogs. We have become aware of the dynamics of our dogs aging. We have focused on geriatric massage and specific therapies designed for you to develop skills to help your dog with respiratory enhancement, upper spine, and hip problems. In addition, we have learned massage terms and advanced techniques as well as some that may be considered more non-traditional. We've discussed what you can do to help your dog live a more HEALTHY, comfortable and stress reduced life.

Enjoy. If you're not having a good time massaging your pet, stop. Chances are, he's not getting much out of it, either. What's happening is you may be too tense and probably need the massage more than he does!

If you're not having a good time massaging your pet, stop.
He's not getting much out of it, either.

To be effective, massage should be a relaxing experience for you both. The attitude you have is transmitted from the center of your back (your heart), down your arms and through your hands to your intuitive receiver. If it doesn't seem to be working, it's not. It takes practice and perseverance to develop these new skills. Take a break. Try again later. It will be better next time.

Thank you for studying this manual. Massage is a skill you'll enjoy using while helping your dog through the remainder of his years. Experiment with the skills you've discovered here. Remember to breathe and listen to your dog. He has a lot to teach. With his support, you will soon develop your own distinct style of massage therapy—one that both you and your dog will find rewarding.

Happy tails,
Jonathan Rudinger, RN, LMT

Part 11 Recipes

Yappetiser-CHEESY HOUND ROUND

½ cup low fat cheddar cheese (shredded)
½ cup low fat cottage cheese
2 ½ tablespoons vegetable oil
2 cups white flour
¾ cup peanuts (chopped)
¼ cup water

Mix together cheddar cheese, flour, cottage cheese, oil and peanuts. Add water and stir. Break off golf ball sized pieces and shape into rounds. Place on a baking sheet that has been sprayed with a non-stick spray. Bake at 375 degrees for 40 minutes. Makes about 24 balls.

Cool and serve. Store in a sealed container in the refrigerator.

Thanks to **Three Dog Bakery** for these recipe contributions.

Three Dog Bakery
1627 Main St., Suite. 700,
Kansas City, MO 64108,
E-mail: info@threedog.com
Internet: www.threedog.com

SNICKER POODLES

½ Cup Canola Oil
½ Cup Shortening
½ Cup Honey
2 Eggs
3 ¾ Cups White Flour
2 tsp. Cream of Tartar
1 tsp. Baking Soda
½ Cup Cornmeal
2 tsp. Cinnamon

In a mixing bowl blend oil, shortening and honey together. Add eggs and beat well. Stir in flour, baking soda and cream of tartar. Knead dough until well mixed. Shape by rounded teaspoons into balls. Mix the cornmeal and cinnamon together and roll each ball in mixture. Place on a cookie sheet that has been sprayed with a non-stick spray. Press balls down with a fork twice going in two different directions. Bake at 400 degrees for 6 minutes. Makes 30.

Cool and store in sealed container.

Thanks to, **Three Dog Bakery.**

BAKED LIVER TREATS

1 lb. liver

Place on cookie sheet. Sprinkle with onion and garlic powder. Bake at 250 degrees 1 hour. Turn and sprinkle other side with onion and garlic and continue baking for another hour.

Let cool and cut in bite size pieces.

Courtesy of, **KDR Distributing**, P O Box 403, Fremont, OH 43420,

1-800-418-0399

Email:kdr@intelliworks.net
Online:www.healthierpet.com

References/Further Reading

Anderson, Robert and Barbara K. Wrede, *Caring for Older Cats and Dogs,* Williamson Publishers, 1990

Beck, Mark F., *Theory and Practice of Therapeutic Massage*, Milady Publishing Company, 1994

Bone, Jesse F., *Animal Anatomy and Physiology,* Prentice Hall, Inc., 1992

Caras, Roger A., *A Dog is Listening,* Summit Books, 1992

Fogle, Bruce, *ASPCA Complete Dog Training Manual,* Darling Kindersley, 1994

Foster, Race and Marty Smith, *What's the Diagnosis*, Howell Book House, 1995

Fox, Michael W., *The Healing Touch*, Newmarket Press, 1990

Fox, Michael W., *The New Animal Doctor's Answer Book,* Newmarket Press, 1984

James, Ruth B., *The Dog Repair Book*, Alpine Press, 1990

Kellogg, John Harvey, *The Art of Massage*, Modern Medicine Publishing Co., 1929

Laureano, Judy, *Golden Retrievers*, T.F.H. Publications, Inc., 1996

Masson, Jeffrey Moussaieff, *Dogs Never Lie About Love*, Crown Publishers, Inc., 1997

McClure, Vimala Schneider, *Infant Massage: a Handbook for Loving Parents*, Bantam Books, 1982

Montagu, Ashley, *Touching*, Harper & Row Publishers, 1971

Roberts, Monty, *The Man Who Listens To Horses*, Random House, 1996

Schwartz, Cheryl, *Four Paws, Five Directions*, Celestial Arts Publishing, 1996

Shively, Michael J., Bonnie Beaver, G., *Dissection of the Dog and Cat*, Iowa State University, 1985

Sobol, Harriet Langsam, *Pet Doctor*, G. P. Putnam's Sons, 1988

Watson, Miller, *Dog Basic Training*, T.F.H. Publications, Inc., 1989

Wilcox, Bonnie and Chris Walkowicz, *Old Dogs, Old Friends*, Macmillan Publishing Company, 1991

Index

Notes